JAMES
MORRI
UNDISCOVE

CHORD
SONGBOOK

WISE PUBLICATIONS
part of The Music Sales Group
London / New York / Paris / Sydney / Copenhagen / Berlin / Madrid / Tokyo

Published by
Wise Publications
14-15 Berners Street, London, W1T 3LJ, UK.

Exclusive distributors:
Music Sales Limited
Distribution Centre, Newmarket Road,
Bury St Edmunds, Suffolk, IP33 3YB, UK.

Music Sales Pty Limited
120 Rothschild Avenue, Rosebery,
NSW 2018, Australia.

Order No. AM990264
ISBN 13: 978-1-84772-047-4
This book © Copyright 2007 Wise Publications,
a division of Music Sales Limited.

Edited by Tom Farncombe.
Music arranged by Matt Cowe.
Music processed by Paul Ewers Music Design.

Printed in the EU.

www.musicsales.com

Your Guarantee of Quality:

As publishers, we strive to produce every book to the highest
commercial standards.

Particular care has been given to specifying acid-free, neutral-sized paper
made from pulps which have not been elemental chlorine bleached.

This pulp is from farmed sustainable forests and was produced
with special regard for the environment.

Throughout, the printing and binding have been planned to ensure
a sturdy, attractive publication which should give years of enjoyment.

If your copy fails to meet our high standards, please inform us
and we will gladly replace it.

You can blame it on me.

Under The Influence

Words & Music by
James Morrison, Jimmy Hogarth & Steve McEwan

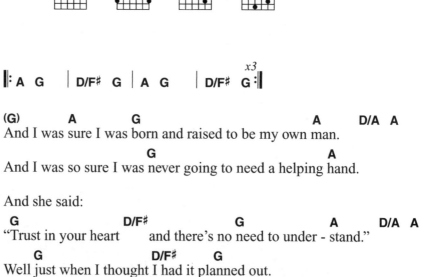

Intro

‖: A G │ D/F♯ G │ A G │ D/F♯ G :‖ *x3*

Verse 1

(G)   A   G   A   D/A A
And I was sure I was born and raised to be my own man.
                             G   A
And I was so sure I was never going to need a helping hand.

And she said:
G   D/F♯   G   A   D/A A
"Trust in your heart   and there's no need to under - stand."
G   D/F♯   G
Well just when I thought I had it planned out.

Chorus 1

        A   G   D/F♯   G   A   G D/F♯ G
What - ever I do I'm under the influence of you.
        A   G   D/F♯   G   A   G D/F♯ G
What - ever I do I'm under the influence of you.

Link 1

│ A │ A │ A │ A ‖

Verse 2

A   G   A
Well I was driving too close to the edge and living dangerously.
                       G   A
I felt strange, a warm sensation rising up in - side of me.
            G   A
Oh like a tidal wave, came from nowhere, swept me off my feet.
        G   D/F♯   G
Oh but somehow making me com - plete now.

	A	G	D/F♯	G	A	G D/F♯ G

Chorus 2

        A   **G**   **D/F♯**   **G**   **A**   **G D/F♯ G**
What - ever I do I'm under the influence of you.

        A   **G**   **D/F♯**   **G**   **A**   **G D/F♯ G**
What - ever I do I'm under the influence of you.

        A   **G**   **D/F♯**   **G**   **A**   **G D/F♯ G**
What - ever I do I'm under the influence of you.

        A   **G**   **D/F♯**   **G**   **A**   **G D/F♯ G**
What - ever I do I'm under the influence of you.

Bridge

A   **G**
Once you've had a taste of it there's no going back.

A   **G**
Once you've had a taste of it there's no going back.

A   **G**
Once you've had a taste of it there's no going back.

A   **G**   **N.C.**
Once you've had a taste of it there's no going back.

Chorus 3

        A   **G**   **D/F♯**   **G**   **A**   **G D/F♯ G**
What - ever I do I'm under the influence of you.

        A   **G**   **D/F♯**   **G**   **A**   **G D/F♯ G**
What - ever I do I'm under the influence of you.

        A   **G**   **D/F♯**   **G**   **A**   **G D/F♯ G**
What - ever I do I'm under the influence of you.

        A   **G**   **D/F♯**   **G**   **A**   **G D/F♯ G**
What - ever I do I'm under the influence of you.

Outro   ‖: **A G** | **(G) D** | **A G** | **(G) D** :‖

You Give Me Something

Words & Music by
Francis White & James Morrison

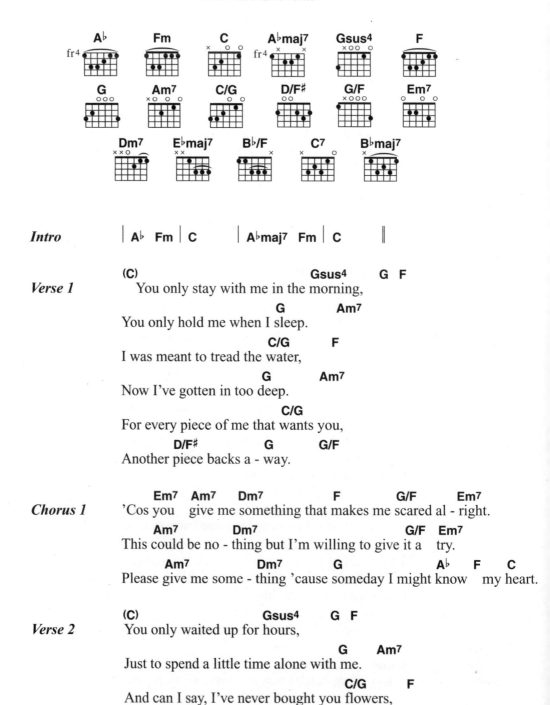

Intro | A♭ Fm | C | A♭maj7 Fm | C   ‖

Verse 1

    (C)   Gsus4   G F
You only stay with me in the morning,
                      G   Am7
You only hold me when I sleep.
                   C/G   F
I was meant to tread the water,
                  G   Am7
Now I've gotten in too deep.
                     C/G
For every piece of me that wants you,
    D/F♯   G   G/F
Another piece backs a - way.

Chorus 1

    Em7 Am7   Dm7   F   G/F   Em7
'Cos you   give me something that makes me scared al - right.
    Am7   Dm7   G/F Em7
This could be no - thing but I'm willing to give it a   try.
    Am7   Dm7   G   A♭ F   C
Please give me some - thing 'cause someday I might know   my heart.

Verse 2

    (C)   Gsus4   G F
You only waited up for hours,
                               G   Am7
Just to spend a little time alone with me.
                                 C/G   F
And can I say, I've never bought you flowers,

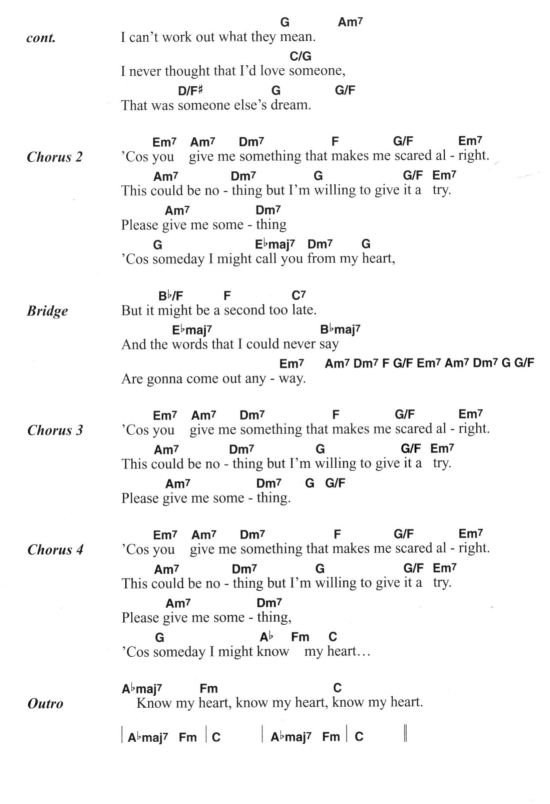

                                G   **Am⁷**

cont.   I can't work out what they mean.

                                      C/G

I never thought that I'd love someone,

                   D/F♯   **G**   **G/F**

That was someone else's dream.

             Em⁷ **Am⁷**   **Dm⁷**   **F**   **G/F**   **Em⁷**

Chorus 2   'Cos you   give me something that makes me scared al - right.

             Am⁷   **Dm⁷**   **G**   **G/F** **Em⁷**

This could be no - thing but I'm willing to give it a   try.

              Am⁷   **Dm⁷**

Please give me some - thing

            G   **E♭maj⁷** **Dm⁷**   **G**

'Cos someday I might call you from my heart,

            B♭/F   **F**   **C⁷**

Bridge   But it might be a second too late.

              E♭maj⁷   **B♭maj⁷**

And the words that I could never say

                                   Em⁷   **Am⁷ Dm⁷ F G/F Em⁷ Am⁷ Dm⁷ G G/F**

Are gonna come out any - way.

             Em⁷ **Am⁷**   **Dm⁷**   **F**   **G/F**   **Em⁷**

Chorus 3   'Cos you   give me something that makes me scared al - right.

             Am⁷   **Dm⁷**   **G**   **G/F** **Em⁷**

This could be no - thing but I'm willing to give it a   try.

              Am⁷   **Dm⁷**   **G** **G/F**

Please give me some - thing.

             Em⁷ **Am⁷**   **Dm⁷**   **F**   **G/F**   **Em⁷**

Chorus 4   'Cos you   give me something that makes me scared al - right.

             Am⁷   **Dm⁷**   **G**   **G/F** **Em⁷**

This could be no - thing but I'm willing to give it a   try.

              Am⁷   **Dm⁷**

Please give me some - thing,

            G   **A♭** **Fm**   **C**

'Cos someday I might know   my heart…

    A♭maj⁷   **Fm**   **C**

Outro   Know my heart, know my heart, know my heart.

| **A♭maj⁷** **Fm** | **C** | | **A♭maj⁷** **Fm** | **C** | ‖

11

Wonderful World

Words & Music by
James Morrison & Eg White

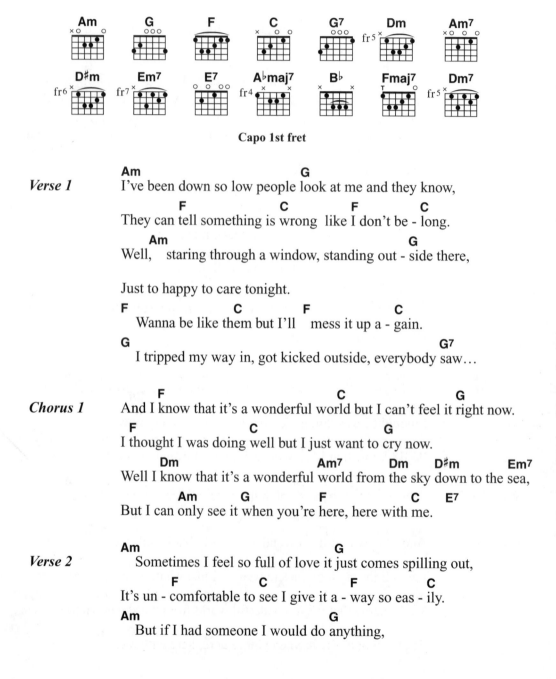

Capo 1st fret

Verse 1

    Am   **G**
I've been down so low people look at me and they know,
          F   **C**   **F**   **C**
They can tell something is wrong like I don't be - long.
       Am   **G**
Well,   staring through a window, standing out - side there,

Just to happy to care tonight.
F   **C**   **F**   **C**
   Wanna be like them but I'll   mess it up a - gain.
G   **G7**
   I tripped my way in, got kicked outside, everybody saw…

Chorus 1

          F   **C**   **G**
And I know that it's a wonderful world but I can't feel it right now.
      F   **C**   **G**
I thought I was doing well but I just want to cry now.
     Dm   **Am7**   **Dm** **D♯m**   **Em7**
Well I know that it's a wonderful world from the sky down to the sea,
        Am   **G**   **F**   **C** **E7**
But I can only see it when you're here, here with me.

Verse 2

   Am   **G**
   Sometimes I feel so full of love it just comes spilling out,
         F   **C**   **F**   **C**
It's un - comfortable to see I give it a - way so eas - ily.
 Am   **G**
   But if I had someone I would do anything,

                                                              F
cont.   And never, never, never, never, let you feel a - lone.
                     C   **F**   **C**
                 I won't, I won't leave you on your own.
                 G   **G⁷**
                     Who am I to dream, dreams are for fools, they let you down.

                         F   **C**   **G**
Chorus 2   And I know that it's a wonderful world but I can't feel it right now.
                     F   **C**   **G**
                 I thought I was doing well but I just want to cry now.
                         Dm   **Am⁷**   **Dm**   **D♯m**   **Em⁷**
                 Well I know that it's a wonderful world from the sky down to the sea,
                         Am   **G**   **F**   **C**   **G**
                 But I can only see it when you're here, here with me.

                 A♭maj⁷   **C**   **B♭**   **A♭maj⁷**
Bridge   And I wish that I could make it bet - ter,
                         B♭   **Fmaj⁷**   **C**
                 I'd give anything   for you to call me.
                             B♭   **A♭maj⁷**
                 Maybe just a little let - ter,
                             Dm⁷   **G**
                 Oh, it could start again.

                         F   **C**   **G**
Chorus 3   And I know that it's a wonderful world but I can't feel it right now.
                     F   **C**   **G**
                 I thought I was doing well but I just want to cry now.
                         Dm   **Am⁷**   **Dm**   **D♯m**   **Em⁷**
                 Well I know that it's a wonderful world from the sky down to the sea,
                         Am   **G**   **F**   **C**   **G**
                 But I can only see it when you're here, here with me.

                         F   **C**   **G**
Chorus 4   And I know that it's a wonderful world but I can't feel it right now.
                     F   **C**   **G**
                 I got all the right clothes to wear,   I just want to cry now, cry now.
                         Dm   **Am⁷**   **Dm**   **D♯m**   **Em⁷**
                 Well I know that it's a wonderful world from the sky down to the sea,
                         Am   **G**   **F**   **C**   **G**
                 But I can only see it when you're here, here with me.

                         Am   **G**   **F**
Outro   And I know that it's a wonderful world,
                 B♭   **C**
                     When you're with me.

13

The Pieces Don't Fit Anymore

Words & Music by
Martin Brammer, Steve Robson & James Morrison

C   Am   F   Dm7

C7   G   E7/G♯   D7   E7

fr3

Capo 1st Fret

Intro | C | C | C | C ‖

Verse 1

C   Am
I've been twisting and turning in a space that's too small,
        C   Am
I've been drawing the line and watching it fall.
              F   C
You've been closing me in, closing the space in my heart,
Am   F   C
Watching us fading and watching it all fall a - part.

Pre-chorus 1

Dm7   F   Dm7
Well I can't explain why it's not enough,
        Am   C7
'Cos I gave it all to you.
            F   Dm7
And if you leave me now, oh just leave me now,
        Am   C7
It's the better thing to do.

Chorus 1

        F
It's time to surrender,
        Dm7
It's been too long pretending.
        Am
There's no use in trying
            C7   F
When the pieces don't fit any - more,
Dm7   C
Pieces don't fit here any - more.

Verse 2

     C   Am
You pulled me under so I had to give in,

     C   Am
Such a beautiful mess that's breaking my skin.

          F   C
Well I'll hide all the bruises, I'll hide all the damage that's done,

Am   F   C
But I show how I'm feeling un - til all the feeling has gone.

Pre-chorus 2   As Pre-chorus 1

Chorus 2   As Chorus 1

Bridge

     G   E7/G♯   Am
  Oh, don't mis - understand how I feel,

          D7   F
'Cos I've tried, yes I've tried.

But still I don't know why,

     E7
No I don't know why,

I don't know why.

Pre-chorus 3

(E7)   F   Dm7
Why I can't explain why it's not enough,

   Am   C7
I gave it all to you.

          F   Dm7
And if you leave me now, just leave me now,

      Am   C7
It's the better thing to do.

Chorus 3

          F
Well it's time to surrender,

        Dm7
It's been too long pretending.

       Am
There's no use in trying

       C7   F
When the pieces don't fit any - more,

      Dm7   C
The pieces don't fit here any - more.

Outro

F   Dm   C
  The pieces don't fit here any - more.

One Last Chance

Words & Music by
Tim Kellett, James Morrison & Kevin Andrews

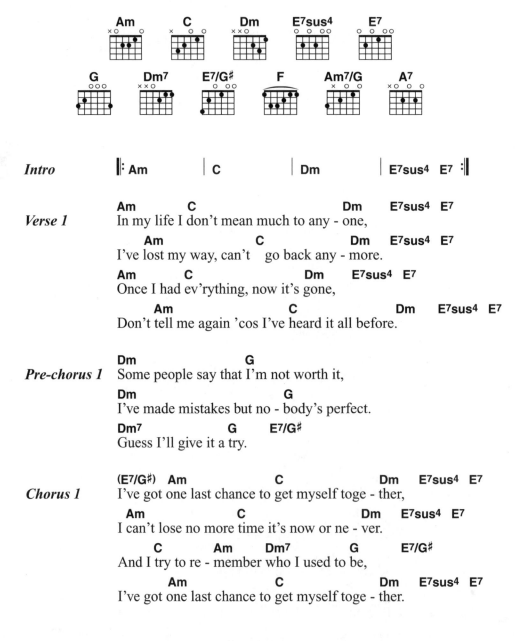

Intro ‖: Am | C | Dm | E⁷sus⁴ E⁷ :‖

Verse 1

Am   C   Dm   E⁷sus⁴ E⁷
In my life I don't mean much to any - one,

　　Am   C   Dm   E⁷sus⁴ E⁷
I've lost my way, can't　go back any - more.

Am   C   Dm   E⁷sus⁴ E⁷
Once I had ev'rything, now it's gone,

　　　Am   C   Dm   E⁷sus⁴ E⁷
Don't tell me again 'cos I've heard it all before.

Pre-chorus 1

Dm   G
Some people say that I'm not worth it,

Dm   G
I've made mistakes but no - body's perfect.

Dm⁷   G   E⁷/G♯
Guess I'll give it a try.

Chorus 1

(E⁷/G♯) Am   C   Dm   E⁷sus⁴ E⁷
I've got one last chance to get myself toge - ther,

　　Am   C   Dm   E⁷sus⁴ E⁷
I can't lose no more time it's now or ne - ver.

　　　C   Am   Dm⁷   G   E⁷/G♯
And I try to re - member who I used to be,

　　　Am   C   Dm   E⁷sus⁴ E⁷
I've got one last chance to get myself toge - ther.

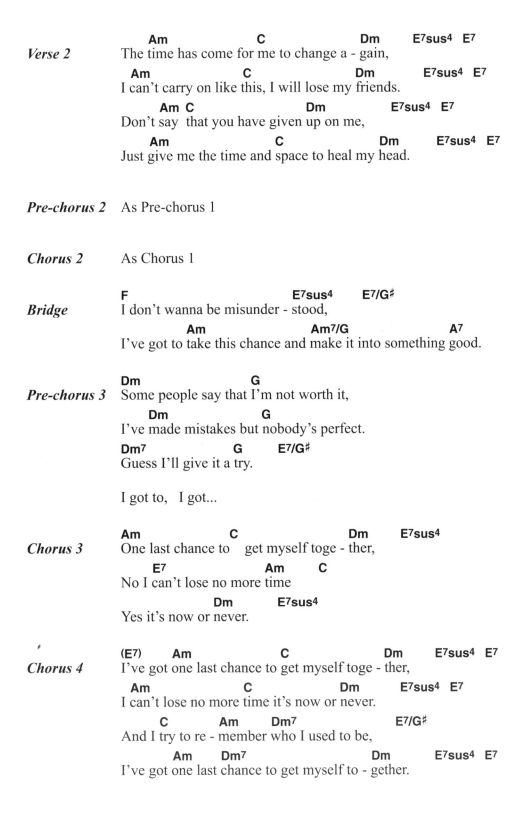

Verse 2

    Am   C   Dm   E7sus4 E7
The time has come for me to change a - gain,

     Am   C   Dm   E7sus4 E7
I can't carry on like this, I will lose my friends.

      Am C   Dm   E7sus4 E7
Don't say that you have given up on me,

     Am   C   Dm   E7sus4 E7
Just give me the time and space to heal my head.

Pre-chorus 2 As Pre-chorus 1

Chorus 2   As Chorus 1

Bridge

F   E7sus4   E7/G♯
I don't wanna be misunder - stood,

         Am   Am7/G   A7
I've got to take this chance and make it into something good.

Pre-chorus 3

Dm   G
Some people say that I'm not worth it,

    Dm   G
I've made mistakes but nobody's perfect.

Dm7   G   E7/G♯
Guess I'll give it a try.

I got to, I got...

Chorus 3

Am   C   Dm   E7sus4
One last chance to   get myself toge - ther,

     E7   Am   C
No I can't lose no more time

           Dm   E7sus4
Yes it's now or never.

Chorus 4

(E7)   Am   C   Dm   E7sus4 E7
I've got one last chance to get myself toge - ther,

    Am   C   Dm   E7sus4 E7
I can't lose no more time it's now or never.

     C   Am   Dm7   E7/G♯
And I try to re - member who I used to be,

     Am   Dm7   Dm   E7sus4 E7
I've got one last chance to get myself to - gether.

Chorus 5

(E7)   **Am**   **C Dm E7sus4**
I've got one last chance,

          E7   **Am**   **C Dm E7sus4**
Well you know it's all I need.

E7   **Am**
One last chance.

Outro

‖: **Am** | **C** | **Dm** | **E7sus4 E7** :‖
  (chance)   *Play 4 times to fade*

The Letter

Words & Music by
David Frank, Wayne Hector & James Morrison

Em   D   G   C   A7   B7

Intro | Em   D | G   C | Em   D | A7   ‖

Verse 1

    Em   D   G
It's got my name on it
               C   Em
And it's just waiting there for me,
                 D   A7   Em
I feel the cold run through my veins.
                   D   G
And it's got her shame on it,
               C   Em
She couldn't say it to my face,
               / D   A7
But I won't waste time placing blame.

Pre-chorus 1

    (A7)   C   G
I know that I'll move on,
  B7   Em   D   C
I tell myself I'll find me something better.
         G   B7
I'll let go and just for - get her.

Chorus 1

    (B7)   C   G
She was no good for me,
     B7   Em   D   C
Deep down I know that's the way it has to be, so
              G   B7
How come I still can't open this letter?
           Em   D G
I can't for - get her.
  C   Em   D A7
Really wish I could.

Verse 2

    Em   D   G
Well there must be a name for it,

                  C   Em
Whatever this is you've done to me,

        D   A^7 Em
I'm all twisted up in - side.

                    D   G
Well who's gonna pay for it?

          C   Em
If it's not you I guess it's me,

                  D   A^7
You left with your life and took mine.

Pre-chorus 2

                  C   G
I know that I'll move on,

      B^7 Em   D   C
I tell myself I'll find me something better.

          G   B^7
I'll let go and just for - get her.

Chorus 2

      B^7 C   G
She was no good for me,

        B^7 Em   D C
Deep down I know that's the way it has to be, so

            G   B^7
How come I still can't open this letter?

            C   G
I can't for - get her.

Bridge

        D   C   Em
Oh I really wish I could

          D   C   G B^7 Em D C
Oh no, really wish I could

G   B^7
Said oh yeah.

Pre-chorus 3

      (B^7)   C   G
And I know that I'll move on,

      B^7 Em   D   C
I tell myself I'll find me something better.

          G   B^7
I'll let go and just for - get her.

	(B7) C G
Chorus 3	She was no good for me,

| B7   Em   D   C |
| Deep down I know that's the way it has to be, so |

| G   B7 |
| How come I still can't open this letter? |

	Em D G
Outro	It's got my name on it

| C |
| And it's just waiting there for me. |

Undiscovered

Words & Music by
Martin Brammer, Steve Robson & James Morrison

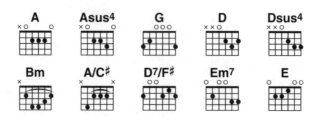

Intro ⏐ A Asus4 ⏐ A Asus4 ⏐ A Asus4 ⏐ A Asus4 ‖

Verse 1

    A   Asus4   A
I look at you, you bite your tongue,

                        G   D   Dsus4 D Dsus4 D
You don't know why or where I'm coming from.

    A   Asus4 A
But in my head I'm close to you,

                      G   D   Dsus4 D Dsus4 D
We're in the rain, still searching for the sun.

Pre-chorus 1

Bm   A/C#   D
  You think that I want to run and hide,

    D7/F#   G   Em7   A
I keep it all locked up in - side, but I just want you to find me.

Chorus 1

       G   A   D
I'm not lost, I'm not lost, just undis - covered.

                    G   A   Bm
And when we're a - lone we are all the same as each other.

    G   A
You see the look that's on my face,

Bm   E
You might think I'm out of place.

      G   A   G   D
I'm not lost, no, no, just undis - covered.

Verse 2

        A   Asus4   A
Well the time it takes to know some - one,

                         G   D   Dsus4 D Dsus4 D
It all can change be - fore you know it's gone.

       A   Asus4   A
So close your eyes and feel the way, I'm with you now,

                       G D   Dsus4   D   Dsus4 D
Believe there's noth - ing wrong,   nothing wrong.

Pre-chorus 2   As Pre-chorus 1

Chorus 2   As Chorus 1

                A
Pre-chorus 3 I'm not running, I'm not hiding,

If you dig a little deeper, you will find me.

                G   A   D
Chorus 3   ‖: I'm not lost, I'm not lost, just undis - covered.

                          G   A   Bm
And when we're a - lone we are all the same as each other.

          G   A
You see the look that's on my face,

Bm   E
You might think I'm out of place.

            G   A   G   D
I'm not lost, no, no, just undis - covered.   :‖

Call The Police

Words & Music by
James Morrison & Eg White

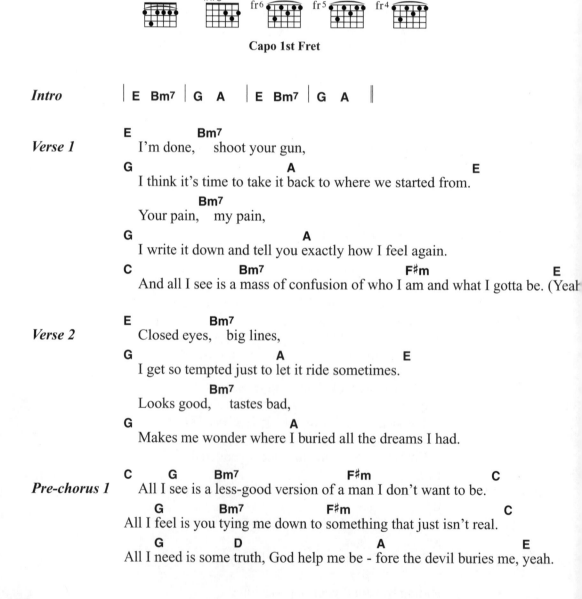

Capo 1st Fret

Intro ‖ E Bm⁷ │ G A │ E Bm⁷ │ G A ‖

Verse 1

E   Bm⁷
I'm done,   shoot your gun,

G   A   E
I think it's time to take it back to where we started from.

Bm⁷
Your pain,   my pain,

G   A
I write it down and tell you exactly how I feel again.

C   Bm⁷   F♯m   E
And all I see is a mass of confusion of who I am and what I gotta be. (Yeah

Verse 2

E   Bm⁷
Closed eyes,   big lines,

G   A   E
I get so tempted just to let it ride sometimes.

Bm⁷
Looks good,   tastes bad,

G   A
Makes me wonder where I buried all the dreams I had.

Pre-chorus 1

C   G   Bm⁷   F♯m   C
All I see is a less-good version of a man I don't want to be.

G   Bm⁷   F♯m   C
All I feel is you tying me down to something that just isn't real.

G   D   A   E
All I need is some truth, God help me be - fore the devil buries me, yeah.

Chorus 1

B♭7   A7   A♭7   E   B♭7
Yeah, I can't do nothing if I can't do something my   way.

         A7   A♭7   E   B♭7
Well I must be crazy if I follow ev'ry word you say.

           A7   A♭7   C
When the shit comes down you'll be the first to walk a - way.

               G   Bm7
Call the po - lice, 'cos I've lost control

        F♯m7   E
And I really want to see you bleed.

Verse 3

E   Bm7
I'm awake,   why wait,

G   A   E
  I don't need someone to tell me who to be today.

            Bm7
I'm quite sure,   unlike before,

G   A
  Came off the road and I for - got what I was looking for.

Pre-chorus 2   As Pre-chorus 1

Chorus 2

B♭7 A7   A♭7   E   B♭7
  I can't do nothing if I can't do something my   way.

         A7   A♭7   E   B♭7
Well I must be crazy if I follow ev'ry word you say.

           A7   A♭7   C
When the shit comes down you'll be the first to walk away.

               G   Bm7
Call the po - lice, 'cos I've lost control

        F♯m7   E   B♭7 A7 A♭7 E B♭7 A7 A♭7
And I really want to see you bleed.

Bridge 1

N.C.
You can't just hack at me, you know, you might just have to let me go.

E   B♭7
Closed in, I need some room to grow,

A7   A♭7   E
  You don't know what you think you know.

            B♭7
Hiding be - hind your pop machine,

A7   A♭7
  So you can break someone else's dream.

Chorus 3

    C   G   Bm7
Call the po - lice 'cos I've lost control
  F#m7   E   B♭7
And I really want to see you bleed.
  A7   A♭7   E   B♭7
I can't do nothing if I can't do something my   way.
  A7   A♭7   E   B♭7
Well I must be crazy if I follow ev'ry word you say.
     A7   A♭7   C
When the shit comes down you'll be the first to walk a - way.

Chorus 4

         G   D
Call the po - lice 'cause I've lost control
     A   C
And I really want to see you bleed.
  G   D   A   C
All I feel is you tying me down to something that just isn't real.
  G   Bm7   F#m7   N.C.
All I need is some truth, god help me be - fore the devil buries me, yeah!

This Boy

Words & Music by
Tim Kellett & James Morrison

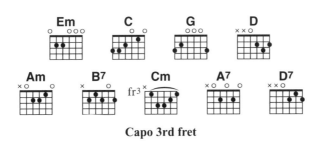

Capo 3rd fret

Intro | Em C | G D | Em C | G D ‖

Verse 1
       Em   **C**   **G**
This boy wants to play, there's no time left to - day,
                  D   **Em**
It's a shame 'cos he has to go home.
                    C
This boy's got to work, got to sweat,
       G   **D**
Just to pay what he gets to get left all alone.

Pre-chorus 1
Am   **C**
But let's step out - side,
        G   **D**   **Am**
Let's go for a ride just for a while.
        C
No we won't get caught,
        G   **D**
Well that's what I thought until we cried.

Chorus 1
      G   **B7**
I'm still here, but it hasn't been easy,
Em   **Cm**   **G**
I'm sure that you had your reasons.
        B7
I'm scared of all this emotion,
Em   **A7**
For years I've been holding it down,
Cm
For years I've been holding it down.

Verse 2

         Em   C
   This girl tries her best every day,

               G   D
But it's all gone to waste 'cos there's no one around.

Em   C   G
   This girl she can draw she can paint, likes to dance she can skate,

               D
Now she don't make a sound.

Pre-chorus 2

         Am   C   G   D
   We'll play in the park till it's too dark for us to see.

Am   C
   Well, we'll make our way home

                      G   D
With mud on our clothes, she won't be pleased.

Chorus 2

            G   B7   Em
   I'm still here, but it hasn't been easy,

               Cm   G
   I'm sure that you had your reasons.

               B7
   I'm scared of all this emotion,

            C   A7
For years I've been holding it down.

Chorus 3

        (A7)   G   B7
And I'd love to for - give and forget,

                 Em   Cm
So I'll   try to put all this behind us.

             G   B7
Just   know that my arms are wide open.

             C   A7   Cm
The older I get the more that I know,

Well it's time to let this go.

Bridge

D7
I got to let it go.

I got to let it go.

I got to let it go.

I got to let it go.

I got to let it go.

I got to let it go.

Chorus 4

(D7)   G   B7   Em
I'm still here, but it hasn't been easy,

                 Cm   G
I'm sure that you had your reasons.

           B7
I'm scared of all this emotion,

        C   A7
For years I've been holding it down.

Chorus 5

           G   B7
And I'd love to for - give and forget,

          Em   Cm
So I'll   try to put all this behind us.

         G   B7
Just   know that my arms are wide open.

        C   A7   Cm
The older I get the more that I know.

Chorus 6

           G   B7
And I'd love to for - give and forget,

          Em   Cm
So I'll   try to put all this behind us.

         G   B7
Just   know that my arms are wide open.

        C   A7   Cm
The older I get the more that I know.

                                G
Well it's time to let this go.

If The Rain Must Fall

Words & Music by
Martin Terefe & James Morrison

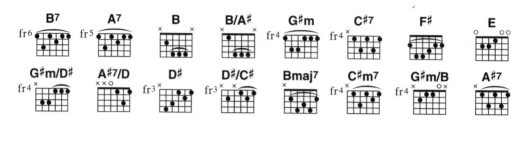

Verse 1

B7   A7   B7   A7
Oh life can be strange, good and bad in so ma - ny ways,

    B   B/A#
And in time you will find that

G#m   C#7 F#
Things are not always what they seem, no.

    B7   A7   B7
Well I've got something to say but you might laugh,

    A7
Joke or run away,

    B   B/A#
'Cos I'm awkward and nervous,

     G#m   C#7 F#
Some - times I don't say much at all.

Chorus 1

(F#)   E   G#m/D#
But if the rain must fall, if I lose it all.

    A#7/D   D#   D#/C#
If the world comes down and takes any soul.

     E   G#m/D#
If the sky turns black and there's no no way back,

    A#7/D   D#   D#/C#
It won't matter much to me if I had you.

Bridge 1

    E   Bmaj7
 And all I need is your love,

       C#m
That's all I need.

       G#m F#
All I need is your love.

Verse 2

(F♯)   B7   A7
Oh well, dreams can come true if you know

     B7   A7
In - side you really want them to,

         B   B/A♯
Or you can sit, you can wait,

        G♯m   C♯7   F♯
You can leave your fate in someone else's hands.

       B7   A7
Oh but I, I want you,

          B7   A7
And nothing else can make me feel the way you do.

       B   B/A♯   G♯m
So I'm waiting, I'm wishing that it's me

             C♯7   F♯
You'll be holding to - night, every night.

Chorus 2

(F♯)   E   G♯m/D♯
But if the rain must fall, if I lose it all.

    A♯7/D   D♯   D♯/C♯
If the world comes down and takes any soul.

     E   G♯m/D♯
If the sky turns black, if there's no no way back,

    A♯7/D   D♯   D♯/C♯
It won't matter much to me if I had you.

Bridge 2

E   Bmaj7
 'Cos all I need is your love,

  C♯m
Oh.

     G♯m   F♯
All I need   is your love, your love.

  C♯m G♯m F♯ C♯m
Oh,——

     G♯m
All I need   is your love.

B7 C♯m
Oh,   that's all I need.

     G♯m   F♯   C♯m
And nothing else, nothing else will ever do,

            G♯m B7
'Cos all I need is you.

Chorus 3

(B7)   E   G♯m/D♯

And if the rain must fall, if I lose it all.

           A♯7/D   D♯   D♯/C♯

If the world comes down and takes any soul.

                E   G♯m/D♯

If the sky turns black, if there's no, no way back,

           A♯7/D   D♯   D♯/C♯

It won't matter much to me if I had you.

Outro

   G♯m/B   A♯7 E   Bmaj7

Oh   ye - ah,   'cos all I need is your love.

The Last Goodbye

Words & Music by
James Morrison, Jimmy Hogarth & Steve McEwan

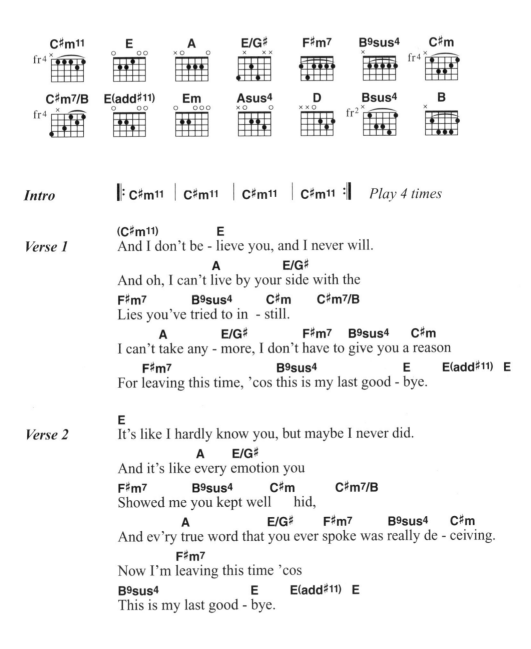

Intro ‖: C#m11 | C#m11 | C#m11 | C#m11 :‖ *Play 4 times*

Verse 1
(C#m11)   E
And I don't be - lieve you, and I never will.
                         A   E/G#
And oh, I can't live by your side with the
F#m7   B9sus4   C#m   C#m7/B
Lies you've tried to in - still.
              A   E/G#   F#m7   B9sus4   C#m
I can't take any - more, I don't have to give you a reason
        F#m7   B9sus4   E   E(add#11) E
For leaving this time, 'cos this is my last good - bye.

Verse 2
              E
It's like I hardly know you, but maybe I never did.
                    A   E/G#
And it's like every emotion you
F#m7   B9sus4   C#m   C#m7/B
Showed me you kept well   hid,
              A   E/G#   F#m7   B9sus4   C#m
And ev'ry true word that you ever spoke was really de - ceiving.
              F#m7
Now I'm leaving this time 'cos
B9sus4   E   E(add#11) E
This is my last good - bye.

Chorus 1

(E)   **Em**
I've gotta turn and walk away,

        A   **Asus4**
I don't have anything left to say

      D
I haven't already said before.

          Em
I've grown tired of being used,

          A   **Asus4**
And I'm sick and tired of being ac - cused.

        F♯m7
Now I'm walking away from you

        Bsus4
And I'm not coming back.

Verse 3

B   **E**
I don't be - lieve you, and I never will.

       A   **E/G♯**
Oh, I can't live by your side with the

F♯m7   **B9sus4**   **C♯m**   **C♯7/B**
Lies you've tried to in - still.

      A   **E/G♯**   **F♯m7**   **B9sus4**   **C♯m**
I can't take any - more, I don't have to give you a reason

      F♯m7
Oh, for leaving this time, 'cos

B11   **E**   **E(add♯11)** **E**
This is my last good - bye.

Chorus 2

(E)   **Em**
Oh I've got - ta turn and walk away,

        A   **Asus4**
I don't have anything left to say

      D
I haven't already said before.

         Em
And I've grown tired of being used,

         A   **Asus4**
And I'm sick and tired of being ac - cused.

        F♯m7
Now I'm walking away from you

      B
And I'm not coming back.

Link ‖: C♯m11 | C♯m11 | C♯m11 | C♯m11 :‖

| E | E | E | E ‖

                        E
Verse 4   And I don't believe you, and I never will.
                              A   E/G♯   F♯m7   B9sus4   C♯m
             Oh I can't take any - more, I don't have to give you a reason
                  F♯m7   B9sus4   E   E(add♯11) E
             For leaving this time, this is my last good - bye.
                                         E(add♯11)   E
             My last goodbye.

How Come

Words & Music by
James Morrison, Jimmy Hogarth & Steve McEwan

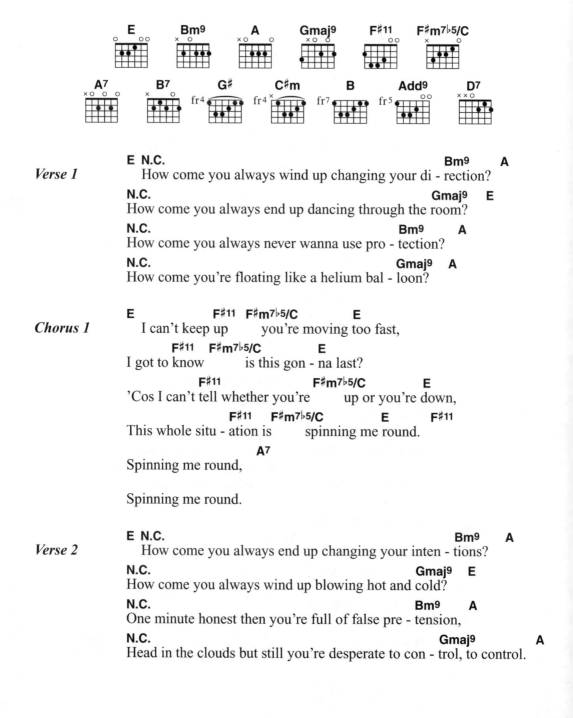

Verse 1

E N.C.   Bm9   A
How come you always wind up changing your di - rection?

N.C.   Gmaj9 E
How come you always end up dancing through the room?

N.C.   Bm9   A
How come you always never wanna use pro - tection?

N.C.   Gmaj9 A
How come you're floating like a helium bal - loon?

Chorus 1

E   F#11 F#m7♭5/C   E
I can't keep up   you're moving too fast,

      F#11 F#m7♭5/C   E
I got to know   is this gon - na last?

      F#11   F#m7♭5/C   E
'Cos I can't tell whether you're   up or you're down,

        F#11 F#m7♭5/C   E   F#11
This whole situ - ation is   spinning me round.

               A7
Spinning me round,

Spinning me round.

Verse 2

E N.C.   Bm9   A
How come you always end up changing your inten - tions?

N.C.   Gmaj9 E
How come you always wind up blowing hot and cold?

N.C.   Bm9   A
One minute honest then you're full of false pre - tension,

N.C.   Gmaj9   A
Head in the clouds but still you're desperate to con - trol, to control.

Chorus 2

E   F#11   F#m7♭5/C   E
  I just don't know   what, what to be - lieve

             F#11   F#m7♭5/C   E
You build me up and then you bring me   down on my knees.

                    F#11   F#m7♭5/C   E
You say you want me   then you're up and you're gone,

     F#11   F#m7♭5/C   E   F#11
I got to know just where you're   coming from.

           A7
Coming from,

                B7
Where you're coming from.

Bridge

G#   C#m   G#
  I got to know before it's over,

One way or the other

     C#m   B   Aadd9
If you're stringing me a - long.

Chorus 3

E   F#11 F#m7♭5/C   E
  I can't keep up   you're moving too fast,

     F#11   F#m7♭5/C E
I got to know is this gonna   last?

       F#11   F#m7♭5/C   E
I can't tell whether you're   up or you're down,

               F#11 F#m7♭5/C   E   F#11
This whole situa - tion is   spinning me round.

                A7
Spinning me round,

                B7
Spinning me round.

            D7
How come?

            E
How come?

N.C.   Bm7
How come you always wind up changing your direc - tion?

Better Man

Words & Music by
Julian Gallagher, James Morrison & Kim Ritchie

F   C   G/B   Am   Gsus4

Fm   D7   C7   E7   G

Fade in

Intro | F | C | C | F | F | C ||

Verse 1
```
C              F                   C
There was a time I had nothing to give,
          F                         C
I needed shelter from the storm I was in.
              G/B       Am      Gsus4
And when it all got too heavy,
                  F
You carried my weight.
              Fm
And I want to hold you,
              D7
And I want to say…
```

Chorus 1
```
          C   C7        E7
That you are all that I need,
      F      D7
For you, I give my soul to keep.
          C    C7       E7
You see me, love me,

Just the way I am.
          F              D7
I said for you I am a better man,
          C            E7
I said you are the reason
          C      Gsus4      F
For ev'ry - thing that I do.
                  G          C      F  C
I'd be lost, so lost, with - out you.
```

Verse 2

    C   **F**   **C**
And under the stars at the edge of the sea,

                   F   **C**
There's no one a - round, no one but you and me.

    G/B   **Am**   **G**
We'd talk for hours,

              F
As time drifts a - way.

                  Fm
I could stay here for - ever

             D7
And hold you this way.

Chorus 2

    C   **C7**   **E7**
'Cos you are all that I need,

   F   **D7**
For you, I give my soul to keep.

    C   **C7**   **E7**
You see me, love me,

Just the way I am.

   F   **D7**
I said for you I am a better man,

   C   **E7**   **Am**
I said you are the reason

     Gsus4   **F**
For ev'ry - thing that I do.

      G   **C**
I'd be lost, so lost, with - out you.

  C7 **E7**
No, no, no.

     F   **G**   **F**   **C**
Oh I'd be lost,   so lost, with - out you.

Don't Close Your Eyes

Words & Music by
Wayne Hector, David Frank & James Morrison

Intro ‖: C#m │ C#m │ Amaj7 │ Amaj7 :‖

Verse 1

        C#sus2   **Asus2**
Well, she's got to smile, she's the wrong side of happy,

                          C#sus2
Too many times she has been let down.

                   Asus2
I tried my best to reach her,

                  F#m
But I guess I'm just too late now.

               G#
She's heard it all be - fore,

             A
Too many times, I'm sure.

              F#
But girl you can't ig - nore

                 E
The world outside your door.

Chorus 1

   (E)   **G#**
Don't close your eyes,

             A
You're missing a good thing.

          F#
Don't close your eyes,

            E   **G#**   **A**
Stick on this ride just one more time.

   F#
It's too early to say goodbye.

Link 1

| C♯m | C♯m |
Don't you say good -

| Amaj⁷ | Amaj⁷ ‖
\- bye.

| C♯m | C♯m |

| Amaj⁷ | Amaj⁷ ‖

Verse 2

(Am⁷) C♯sus2   Asus2
Well,   she sees the world through the eyes of her mother,

                                                          C♯sus2
There's always room, room to criticize.

                                                    Asus2
Every man, a potential lover

                                            F♯m
And ev'ry girl, a demon in dis - guise.

                                      G♯
She thinks she knows you're game,

                            A
Like ev'ryone's the same,

                          F♯
Like ev'ryone's to blame.

                        E
Well baby it's a shame.

Chorus 2   As Chorus 1

Link 2

| C♯m | C♯m | Amaj⁷ ‖

Amaj⁷   C♯m
Don't you say good - bye.

                      Amaj⁷
Don't you say goodbye.

                            F♯m
Oh, no it's not time.

Verse 3   F♯m   G♯
There's poison in your veins,

                      A
When will you let it out

                      F♯
Upon a scream and shout?

                     E
Start what life's a - bout.

Chorus 3   As Chorus 1

Outro   ‖: C♯m | C♯m | Amaj⁷ | Amaj⁷ :‖   *Play 15 times w/vocal ad lib.*

            | C♯m   ‖

Is Anybody Home?

Words & Music by
Martin Terefe & James Morrison

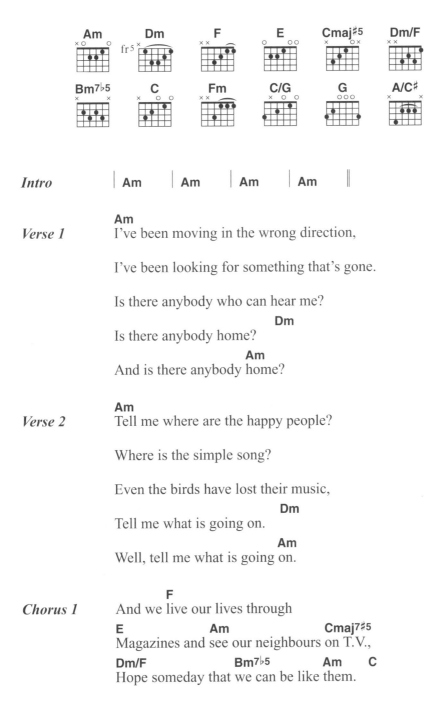

Intro

| Am | Am | Am | Am |

Verse 1

Am
I've been moving in the wrong direction,

I've been looking for something that's gone.

Is there anybody who can hear me?
                 Dm
Is there anybody home?
            Am
And is there anybody home?

Verse 2

Am
Tell me where are the happy people?

Where is the simple song?

Even the birds have lost their music,
                Dm
Tell me what is going on.
                Am
Well, tell me what is going on.

Chorus 1

       F
And we live our lives through
E   **Am**   **Cmaj7♯5**
Magazines and see our neighbours on T.V.,
Dm/F   **Bm7♭5**   **Am**   **C**
Hope someday that we can be like them.

cont.

        F   **Fm**
And ain't it sad that deep inside we
C   **Cmaj7♯5**
Lost ourselves and don't know why,
  Dm/F   **Bm7♭5**   **Am**   **C/G**
I look up to the sky when I'm a - lone
        F   **G**   **Am**
And I wonder is there anybody home?

Am
Verse 3 Ev'rybody gonna say it's crazy,

They say that it can't be done.

When did we all stop dreaming
                       Dm
About a world where ev'ryone be - longs,
               Am
Yeah, where ev'ryone be - longs.

Am
Verse 4 Our children have lost their childhood,

Their mothers have lost their strength.

Our father's gotta keep on working
                    Dm
Till the day the money's spent,
          Am
Oh,   before he drop and die.

          F   **E**
Chorus 2 Oh, we turn our back on what is real,
     Am   **Cmaj7♯5**
We don't even know how it feels,
Dm/F   **Bm7♭5**   **Am**   **C**
Really want to buy a bigger car.
      F   **Fm**
Baby, ain't it true that deep in you
    C   **Cmaj7♯5**
This feeling lives and lingers too,
  Dm/F   **Bm7♭5**   **Am**   **C/G**
You look up to the sky when you're a - lone
        F   **G**   **F**
And you wonder is there anybody home?

Link

|| F | F | |
(home)
| Dm | Dm G | Am | Am C |

| Dm | Dm G | Am | C/G ||

Bridge

A/C♯   Dm
Tell me, tell me, tell me what is going on.

Chorus 3

Dm   E
When we live our lives through magazines,
      Am   Cmaj7♯5
We see our neighbours on T.V.,
Dm/F   Bm7♭5   Am   C
Hope someday that we can be like them.
   F   Fm
But ain't it sad that deep inside we
C   Cmaj7♯5
Lost ourselves and don't know why,
   Dm/F   Bm7♭5   Am   C/G
I look up to the sky when I'm a - lone
      F   G   F
And I wonder is there anybody home?
      G   Am
Is there anybody home?

Outro

||: Am | Am | Am | Am :|| *Play 4 times ad lib.*
(home)

My Uprising

Words & Music by
James Hogarth, James Morrison & Steve McEwan

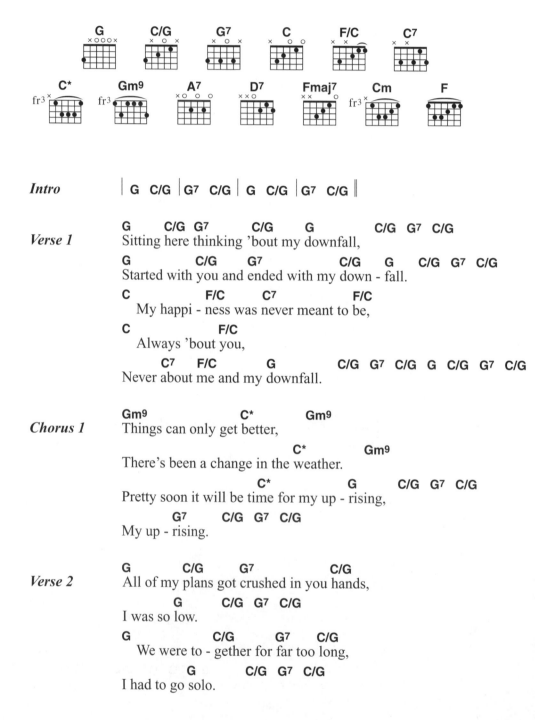

Intro | G C/G | G7 C/G | G C/G | G7 C/G ‖

Verse 1

G   C/G G7   C/G   G   C/G G7 C/G
Sitting here thinking 'bout my downfall,

G   C/G   G7   C/G   G   C/G G7 C/G
Started with you and ended with my down - fall.

C   F/C   C7   F/C
   My happi - ness was never meant to be,

C   F/C
   Always 'bout you,

      C7   F/C   G   C/G G7 C/G G C/G G7 C/G
Never about me and my downfall.

Chorus 1

Gm9   C*   Gm9
Things can only get better,

                    C*   Gm9
There's been a change in the weather.

               C*   G   C/G G7 C/G
Pretty soon it will be time for my up - rising,

     G7   C/G G7 C/G
My up - rising.

Verse 2

G   C/G   G7   C/G
All of my plans got crushed in you hands,

       G   C/G G7 C/G
I was so low.

G   C/G   G7   C/G
  We were to - gether for far too long,

       G   C/G G7 C/G
I had to go solo.

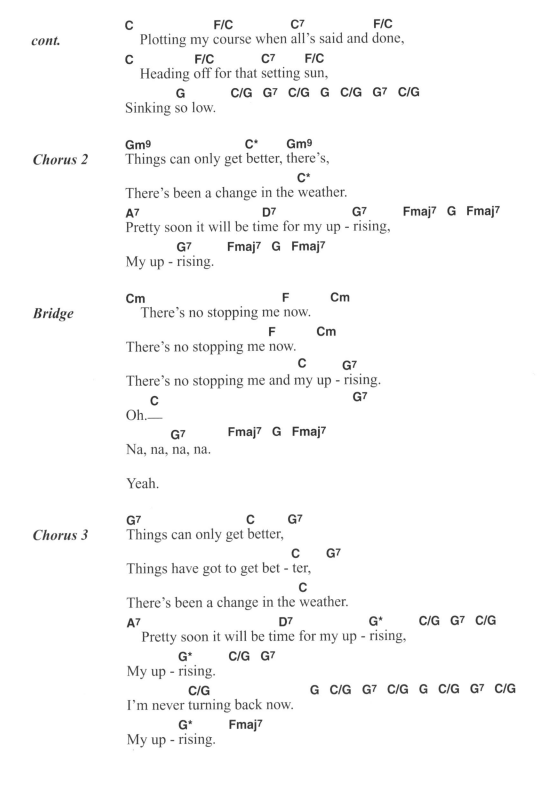

```
            C           F/C          C7              F/C
cont.           Plotting my course when all's said and done,
            C         F/C         C7      F/C
                Heading off for that setting sun,
                 G        C/G  G7  C/G  G  C/G  G7  C/G
                Sinking so low.

            Gm9                      C*      Gm9
Chorus 2    Things can only get better, there's,
                                         C*
            There's been a change in the weather.
            A7                   D7              G7       Fmaj7  G  Fmaj7
            Pretty soon it will be time for my up - rising,
                 G7        Fmaj7  G  Fmaj7
            My up - rising.

            Cm                        F       Cm
Bridge          There's no stopping me now.
                                      F       Cm
            There's no stopping me now.
                                     C      G7
            There's no stopping me and my up - rising.
                 C                               G7
            Oh.—
                 G7        Fmaj7  G  Fmaj7
            Na, na, na, na.

            Yeah.

            G7                  C      G7
Chorus 3    Things can only get better,
                                  C      G7
            Things have got to get bet - ter,
                                     C
            There's been a change in the weather.
            A7                      D7             G*      C/G  G7  C/G
                Pretty soon it will be time for my up - rising,
                 G*       C/G  G7
            My up - rising.
                 C/G                   G  C/G  G7  C/G  G  C/G  G7  C/G
            I'm never turning back now.
                 G*       Fmaj7
            My up - rising.
```

47

Relative Tuning

The guitar can be tuned with the aid of pitch pipes or dedicated electronic guitar tuners which are available through your local music dealer. If you do not have a tuning device, you can use relative tuning. Estimate the pitch of the 6th string as near as possible to E or at least a comfortable pitch (not too high, as you might break other strings in tuning up). Then, while checking the various positions on the diagram, place a finger from your left hand on the:

5th fret of the E or 6th string and **tune the open A** (or 5th string) to the note Ⓐ

5th fret of the A or 5th string and **tune the open D** (or 4th string) to the note Ⓓ

5th fret of the D or 4th string and **tune the open G** (or 3rd string) to the note Ⓖ

4th fret of the G or 3rd string and **tune the open B** (or 2nd string) to the note Ⓑ

5th fret of the B or 2nd string and **tune the open E** (or 1st string) to the note Ⓔ

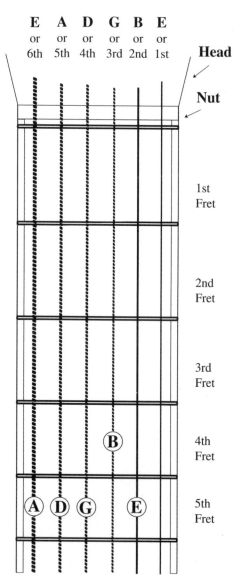

Reading Chord Boxes

Chord boxes are diagrams of the guitar neck viewed head upwards, face on as illustrated. The top horizontal line is the nut, unless a higher fret number is indicated, the others are the frets.

The vertical lines are the strings, starting from E (or 6th) on the left to E (or 1st) on the right.

The black dots indicate where to place your fingers.

Strings marked with an O are played open, not fretted. Strings marked with an X should not be played.

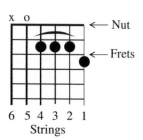

The curved bracket indicates a 'barre' - hold down the strings under the bracket with your first finger, using your other fingers to fret the remaining notes.

123456789